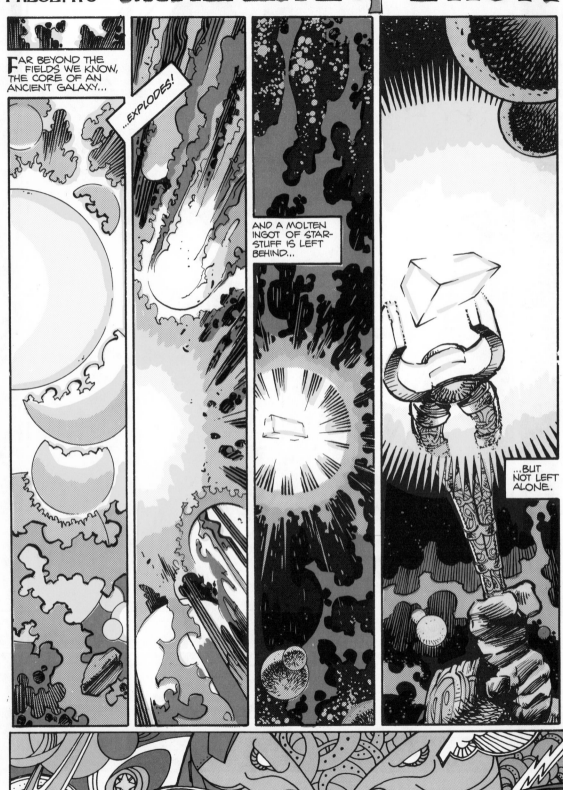

STAN LEE PRESENTS: the MIGHTY THOR®

FAR BEYOND THE FIELDS WE KNOW, THE CORE OF AN ANCIENT GALAXY...

...EXPLODES!

AND A MOLTEN INGOT OF STAR-STUFF IS LEFT BEHIND...

...BUT NOT LEFT ALONE.

THE MIGHTY THOR

THE BALLAD OF BETA RAY BILL

WALTER SIMONSON
writer/artist/designer

JOHN WORKMAN
letterer

GEORGE ROUSSOS
colorist

MARK GRUENWALD
editor

RALPH MACCHIO
MIKE ROCKWITZ
reprint editors

introduction

The ballad of Beta Ray Bill began as an idea.

I had been asked by then editor Mark Gruenwald to take over Thor as both writer and artist and I wanted to start my work on the title with something unusual, something different, something unique. Something that had never been done in THOR before.

My model for such a beginning came from the work that Jack Kirby had done for DC Comics some thirteen years earlier. When Jack began his Fourth World tetralogy for DC, he took the comic, JIMMY OLSEN, and revamped it completely. His first issue of Superman's pal was as different from the preceding issues as chalk is from cheese! The issue was riveting. It exploded with new ideas, new characters, new situations. I didn't have as many ideas as Jack; no one does. But I definitely wanted to begin my run on Thor with as dramatic a break from the preceding issues as I possibly could.

Thor's enchanted hammer seemed like the right place to start. Besides Thor and Odin, no one had ever been able to lift it. The enchantment of the hammer as longtime readers know decreed that "Whosoever holds this hammer, if he be worthy, shall possess the power of Thor." It seemed like a good place to start. And that meant finding someone to hold the hammer who was not only worthy, but interesting, a character full of his own innate nobility, tragedy, and responsibilities. This was no opportunity to waste on some parochial hero.

Visually, Bill was designed to play against type. American comics are primarily a short story form. As a result, symbols are used relentlessly as an aid to shorthand communications in the medium. Which means that in the main, good guys look like good guys, and bad guys look like bad guys. An Adonis-like god who came to Earth and picked up Thor's hammer would surprise no one. A monster who did the same thing would be startling. I needed a monster. At the same time, the underlying nobility of the character could still be suggested. Bill's face was designed with a horse skull in mind. Few animals are so noble or beautiful as the horse.

Bill's name was another matter. I wanted a common name, a symbol of the hero's identification with every man, even if he himself was quite unique. And I also wanted something with a slightly SF flavor. I had in fact originally thought of calling him "Beta Ray Jones" since Jones is such a stereotypical last name but felt that as Marvel already had several Joneses in various comics (and editorial positions), I'd best look elsewhere for a name. And I liked the alliteration.

From such considerations was Beta Ray Bill born, a character unique even among his own kind, a combination of savior and pariah, noble enough to sacrifice himself and his happiness for his people, human enough to be hurt by their rejection.

Most comics are a team effort and THOR was no exception. Thanks are due Mark Gruenwald and Mike Carlin who helped on the editorial side of the book. And I'd like to give a note of special appreciation to John Workman, whose distinctive lettering and sound effects gave the book so much of its graphic quality. Without the efforts of these fine folks, Bill's realization would have been a good deal less effective.

October 8, 1989

THE MIGHTY THOR®: The Ballad Of Beta Ray Bill.™ Originally published in magazine form as The Mighty Thor #337-340. Published by Marvel Comics, 387 Park Avenue South, New York, N.Y. 10016. Copyright © 1983, 1989 by Marvel Entertainment Group, Inc. All rights reserved. THE MIGHTY THOR, "The Ballad of Beta Ray Bill" and all prominent characters appearing herein and the distinctive likenesses thereof, are trademarks of Marvel Entertainment Group, Inc. No part of this book may be printed or reproduced in any manner whatsoever whether mechanical or electronic, without written permission of the publisher.

Printed in the UNITED STATES OF AMERICA

First Printing: December 1989

ISBN# 0-87135-614-7

THE SOUND OF THUNDER REVERBERATES THROUGHOUT A BILLION BILLION WORLDS.

DOOM!

WHY NOT LET US BE THE JUDGES OF THAT, MISTER. A LAME GUY LIKE YOURSELF--YOU LOOK LIKE YOU COULD USE SOME HELP.

LET ME TAKE YOUR CANE.

HEY!

NOT TOO LOUD NOW, BUB. YOU'RE JUST GOING FOR A LITTLE RIDE.

THROW THE STICK IN, TOO, BOYS.

SURE THING, COLONEL.

YOU'RE ALL SET, SIR.

SLAM!

ANY IDEA WHAT'S GOING ON?

BEATS ME.

VARROOOOM!

WHAT DO YOU THINK YOU'RE--

COLONEL NICK FURY!

YOU WIN THE KEWPIE DOLL, DOCTOR BLAKE.

SORRY TA GRAB YA SO DRAMATIC-LIKE, BUT WE NEED YER HELP ...FAST!

HOLD ON TA YER HELMET.

I'M CONVERTIN' TA AERIAL MODE!

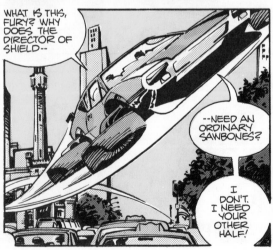

WHAT IS THIS, FURY? WHY DOES THE DIRECTOR OF SHIELD--

--NEED AN ORDINARY SAWBONES?

I DON'T. I NEED YOUR OTHER HALF!

WHAT DO YOU MEAN?

LOOK, DOC, I'LL LEVEL WITH YA.

WE GOT AN EMERGENCY ON OUR HANDS LIKE WE AIN'T SEEN BEFORE.

ONLY ONE GUY I KNOW OF CAN MAYBE HANDLE IT.

AND HE PACKS A HAMMER THAT MAKES OUR LATEST WEAPONS LOOK LIKE TINKERTOYS!

SHORTLY, IN A DARKENED SHIELD SCREENING ROOM...

SITWELL'S OUR LOCAL ENCYCLOPEDIA. IF HE DON'T KNOW IT, IT AIN'T A FACT!

OKAY, SITWELL, FILL IN OUR GUEST AND MAKE IT SNAPPY, HUH?

WELL, SIR, YOUR HONOR... AHEM... THIS IS THE VERY LATEST DEVELOPMENT FROM OUR TELEMETRY DIVISION.

AN EXPERIMENTAL WARP-DRIVEN PROBE CAPABLE OF COVERING UNIMAGINABLE DISTANCES AND TRANSMITTING PICTURES INSTANTANEOUSLY VIA HYPER-WAVE BACK TO A RECEIVER.

NAMELY US.

OPERATING ON AN ASSIGNED CARRIER FREQUENCY OF--

THE GUTS, SITWELL, JUST THE GUTS!

YESSIR! THESE ARE THE LAST PICTURES WE RECEIVED FROM THE PROBE. NOTE THE APPARENT VESSEL IN CENTER SCREEN.

AN ALIEN SHIP, UNLIKE ANYTHING WE'VE EVER SEEN BEFORE.

NOW WATCH THE STAR.

AS THE SHIP PASSED BY IT, THE STAR SUDDENLY FLARED TO LIFE...

...AND WAS SUCKED IN BY THE SHIP.

OUR EXPERTS THINK THE VESSEL WAS REFUELING AND DESTROYED AN ENTIRE STAR TO DO IT.

SHORTLY THEREAFTER, THE PROBE WAS DETECTED BY THE ALIEN SHIP AND ALL TRANSMISSION CEASED.

ACCORDING TO OUR BEST ESTIMATES, THE SHIP IS TRAVELING AT SEVERAL TIMES LIGHT SPEED...

...HEADING DIRECTLY FOR OUR SOLAR SYSTEM.

AND THE PROBE?

DEADER'N A DOORNAIL, THOR. BLOWN APART BY SOMETHING COMING OUR WAY.

SOMETHING REAL POWERFUL! AND DANGEROUS!

WE GOTTA FIND OUT WHAT IT IS! AND YER THE ONLY JOE WHO CAN DO IT!

WILL YA HELP US?

BRAVE BALDER, I RETURN TO ASGARD FROM EARTH ONLY TO FIND YOU IN THE MEAD HALL WITH VOLSTAGG THE ENORMOUS, FEASTING WITHOUT RESPITE!

THOR HAS FORSAKEN ME FOR MIDGARD.*

*EARTH.

MY HEART, MY SOUL ARE EMPTY.

I NEED YOUR STRENGTH, YOUR UNDER-STANDING, YOUR TENDERNESS...

THEN SEEK SOLACE ELSEWHERE, LADY. BALDER THE BRAVE IS NO MORE.

HE WHO HAS RETURNED FROM HELA'S DARK DOMAIN IS NOT FIT TO BE A MAN MUCH LESS A GOD!

I HAVE FORSWORN ALL BATTLES SAVE THIS ONE—THAT I WILL FORGET EVERYTHING I HAVE EVER CHERISHED...

...DEFEATING AT LAST THE FEARFUL CURSE OF THE MEMORY OF THE GOD I ONCE WAS.

ETERNITY IS A LONG TIME, MILADY. BALDER THE BRAVE IS A MYTH I HAVE OUTLIVED.

SOMEONE APPROACHES HEIMDALL THE WATCHER.

BY WHOSE LEAVE DO YOU TREAD UPON BIFROST, THE RAINBOW BRIDGE?

IT IS I, SIF. I HAVE COME BECAUSE I HAVE NOWHERE ELSE TO TURN.

SIF, DEAR SISTER, I HAVE HEARD YOUR TROUBLES. WHAT WOULD YOU HAVE ME DO?

I AM A SHIELD MAIDEN, MY BROTHER. YOUR EYES AND EARS SEE AND HEAR ALL THINGS.

WHITHER CAN I FIND THE CLASH OF BATTLE TO MAKE ME HAPPY AND EASE MY EMPTINESS?

MY POOR DAR-LING. MAYHAP ONLY ODIN HIMSELF CAN HELP YOU NOW.

MEANWHILE, A LONG WAY FROM EARTH...

THE POWER OF MY ENCHANTED MALLET TO CROSS TIME AND SPACE HAS BROUGHT ME CLOSE TO THE ALIEN VESSEL...

...AND RESTORED MY FAITH IN MY HERITAGE! WHAT MORTAL COULD DO WHAT I HAVE DONE?

'TIS GOOD TO BE THE GOD OF THUNDER!

ODIN'S BLOOD! THE SHIP OUTRACES ME AS THE HARE OUTRACES THE TORTOISE!

I MUST INCREASE MY SPEED A HUNDREDFOLD IF I AM TO OVERTAKE YON VESSEL.

BUT OVERTAKE IT I SHALL!

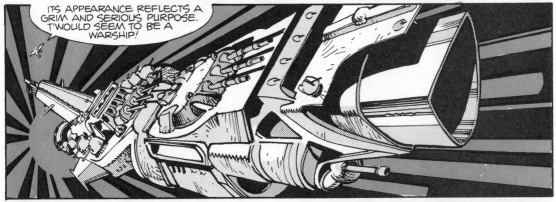

ITS APPEARANCE REFLECTS A GRIM AND SERIOUS PURPOSE. T'WOULD SEEM TO BE A WARSHIP!

CHIKCHIKCHIK

SENSORS DETECT UNIDENTIFIED PURSUER ON INTERCEPT COURSE. ENERGY CONFIGURATIONS SIMILAR TO DEMON BREED. PREPARE TO OPEN FIRE.

MAIN BATTERIES CHARGED AND READY.

TARGET LOCKED MAGNIFICATION THREE.

TARGET CLOSING.

FIRE!

BY THE GOLDEN SPIRES OF ASGARD!

AN ENERGY BOLT OF PURE FORCE!

CLIKCLIK

THIS DEMON IS MUCH STRONGER THAN PREVIOUS INTRUDERS!

ALL BATTERIES OPEN FIRE!

AGAIN THE VESSEL DIRECTS AN UNPROVOKED ATTACK AT ME!

SO BE IT!

LET THE HAMMER OF THOR SPEAK FOR ME NOW!

THRAAKK!

AS EVER, MY HAMMER RETURNS TO ME...

...AND NOW, BEFORE A FURTHER ATTACK CAN BEGIN...

...I SHALL AVOID THE DEADLY WEAPONRY AND ENTER THE SHIP AS ONLY THE GOD OF THUNDER CAN!

PERHAPS INSIDE I CAN DISCOVER THE PURPOSE OF THIS DEADLY VESSEL.

ALL AROUND ME I CAN HEAR THE HUM OF THE MIGHTY STAR-DRIVEN EN-GINES...

...WHILE BEHIND ME, THE HULL SEALS ITSELF SHUT LIKE A LIVING THING!

BUT IF THIS IS TRULY A LIVING MECH-ANISM, THEN SURELY THAT CRYSTAL MUST BE ITS HEART!

YET WHAT LIES HERE AT ITS VERY CENTER?

A FIGURE OF SOME SIZE.

PERHAPS-- EH?

CHIKCHIK

DANGER! DANGER!

INTRUDER HAS BREACHED THE HULL!

ULTIMATE DEFENSE PROCEDURE!

RELEASE COLDSLEEP DEFENSE!

KRASH!

UGGH!

BUT EVEN AS THOR STRUGGLES FOR BREATH, LET US TURN TO A DESOLATE CORNER OF ASGARD TO FIND...

TO THINK THAT LOKI, PRINCE OF DARKNESS, SHOULD WASTE HIS TIME IN MONOTONOUS EXILE WHILE CHEER AND GOOD FELLOWSHIP ABOUND IN THE LAND.

I AM BORED TO DEATH!

BAH! I'VE HALF A MIND TO...

...BUT SOFTLY! WHAT'S THIS I HEAR?

WHO DARES TO PASS SO CLOSE TO LOKI'S LONELY ABODE?

"SO! A FEW LACKWIT WARRIORS VENTURE TO ENGAGE IN A FORBIDDEN TROLL HUNT!"

"I BELIEVE THE END OF MY BOREDOM IS AT HAND!"

PUFF PUFF

MUST HIDE! MUST HIDE! OR HUNTERS SLAY ME!

DID YOU SEE?

YES, HELGI, THE TROLL'S GONE TO COVER IN THOSE THISTLES!

BY YMIR'S BEARD, WE MAY NEVER FLUSH HIM NOW!

LITTLE ONE! PSST! LITTLE ONE!

HUH?

DO NOT BE AFRAID, LITTLE TROLL. I CAN HELP YOU. I CAN HIDE YOU.

IT GIRL! SHE...SHE BEAUTIFUL!

COME. LOOK AT ME. GIVE ME YOUR HAND...

...AND FEAR NOTHING.

LOOK AT ME.

I...

WHITHER AWAY, MY LORDS?

WHA--?

IT'S LORELEI! WITH THE TROLL! SHE'S WON THE HUNT!

JUST AS I FORETOLD YOU!

WEAPONS AND STRENGTH ARE NOT EVERYTHING, MY LORDS.

INDEED, MILADY. AS NONE KNOW BETTER THAN I.

I THINK WE SHOULD DISCUSS THIS FURTHER. WILL YOU NOT ACCOMPANY ME BACK TO MY HUMBLE DWELLING?

PERHAPS I SHALL, MY LORD.

LORELEI, YOU'D BEST LEAVE WITH US. THE OPEN HAND OF LOKI IS NOT SAFE!

NOR WILL YOU BE SAFE IF ODIN LEARNS OF THIS HUNT! LEAVE US AND FORGET WHAT HAS HAPPENED HERE...

...OR THE NEXT HAND OF LOKI YOU SEE WILL BE FILLED WITH MENACE.

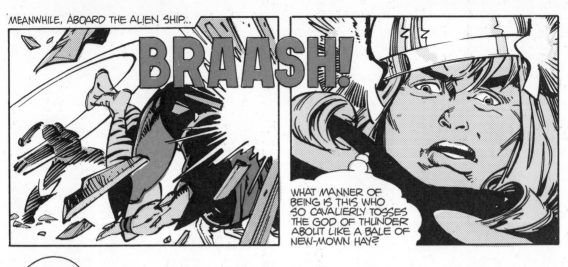

BRAASH!

WHAT MANNER OF BEING IS THIS WHO SO CAVALIERLY TOSSES THE GOD OF THUNDER ABOUT LIKE A BALE OF NEW-MOWN HAY?

RISE UP, DEMON!

YOU HAVE PURSUED ME ONLY TO FIND DEATH!

AND WHEN I AM THROUGH WITH YOU, YOU WILL WELCOME IT!

I AM CALLED BILL--BETA RAY BILL!

BUT DO NOT TROUBLE YOUR-SELF TO REMEMBER IT!

YOU SHOULD HAVE WAITED FOR YOUR FELLOWS TO ARRIVE RATHER THAN FACE ME ALONE!

I DO NOT KNOW WHAT YOU MEAN, CREATURE...

...BUT NONE MAY TOUCH THE MIGHTY THOR SO WITHOUT PAYING THE PRICE!

YET HOW IS IT YOU SPEAK MY TONGUE?

AAGGH!

THE SHIP WAS RIGHT! YOU ARE MUCH STRONGER THAN YOUR PREDECESSORS!

APPARENTLY THE BREED IS IMPROVING!

BUT IT WILL NOT SAVE YOU!

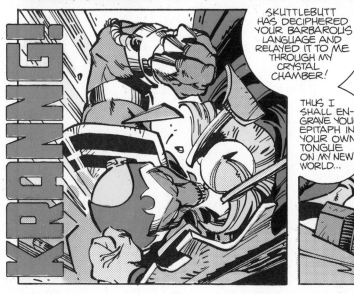

KRANNG!

SKUTTLEBUTT HAS DECIPHERED YOUR BARBAROUS LANGUAGE AND RELAYED IT TO ME THROUGH MY CRYSTAL CHAMBER!

THUS I SHALL EN-GRAVE YOUR EPITAPH IN YOUR OWN TONGUE ON MY NEW WORLD...

...ON THE MEMORIAL CELEBRATING MY VICTORY OVER YOU AND ALL OF DEMONKIND!

YOU STILL SPEAK IN RIDDLES, WARRIOR...

...EVEN IF I MUST DESTROY THIS SHIP FROM WITHIN TO STOP YOU!

...BUT IT IS CLEAR TO ME THAT I CAN NEVER PERMIT SUCH A DANGEROUS ENTITY TO REACH EARTH...

CHIKCHIK

INTERNAL MONITORS INDICATE GRAVE DAMAGE TO SURVIVAL AND WEAPONS SYSTEMS.

CURSÉD DEMON! YOUR DEATH WILL BE AN UNCLEAN ONE FOR THIS DELAY!

IMMEDIATE LANDING NECESSARY TO EFFECT REPAIRS. BEGIN INSTRUMENT SEARCH FOR POTENTIAL SITES!

CHIKCHIK

SEARCH COMPLETE. ACCEPTABLE PLANETARY SYSTEM AHEAD.

PRELIMINARY SCAN INDICATES THIRD PLANET CONTAINS NECESSARY MATERIAL FOR REPAIRS.

CHANGE COURSE TO SEVEN-- GAMMA--Y-- SEVEN.

NEVER HAVE I BEEN SO WELL MATCHED BY ANY MORTAL, BUT THOUGH I RELISH THE STRUGGLE, IT MUST END NOW!

WILL YOU YIELD, WARRIOR?

ONLY IN *DEATH!*

CHIKCHIK

LANDING MODE CONFIRMED.

SHIP NOW ENTERING THE PLANE OF THE ECLIPTIC OF THE THIRD PLANET.

YOU LEAVE ME NO CHOICE. I MUST--

BY MY TROTH!

WHAT *WEAKNESS* SUDDENLY ASSAILS ME?

OH, NO! NOT NOW! NOT LIKE THIS!

WE MUST BE CLOSING FAST WITH EARTH AND WITHOUT MY HAMMER IN MY HAND, I'VE REVERTED TO MY BLAKE FORM!

I'VE GOT TO--

YOU'LL DO NOTHING, DEMON!

YOU MAY HAVE CHANGED YOUR SHAPE... BUT IT CERTAINLY SEEMS ILL SUITED FOR COMBAT!

UHHH!

HEADS UP IN THE SHIP! THIS IS NICK FURY, DIRECTOR OF SHIELD TALKIN' AT YA!

WE GOT YA SURROUNDED! WADDYA SAY YOU COME OUT PEACEABLE AND WE'LL TALK!

THE DEMON'S WEAPON! THE HAMMER HE WIELDED SO POWERFULLY!

IT COULD BE MY ONLY CHANCE TO SAVE MY MISSION!

BUT WHERE...?

WHAT'S THIS? A STICK?

THE HAMMER HAS VANISHED!

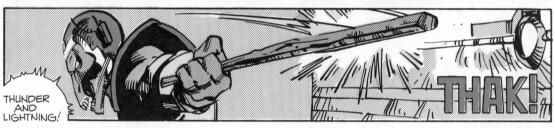

THUNDER AND LIGHTNING!

THAK!

WHA--?!

I...I HAVE THE POWER! THE STICK WAS THE HAMMER!

AND NOW I...I CAN FEEL THE POWER OF THE DEMON HIMSELF ADDED TO MY OWN!

POWER ENOUGH TO SHAKE THIS PLANET TO ITS FOUNDATIONS!

BARROOOOM!

HE'S GONE! THEY'RE BOTH GONE!

AND I GOT A FEELIN' SOMEBODY'S GETTIN' THE SURPRISE OF THEIR LIFE RIGHT ABOUT NOW!

BUT THAT SHIP'S STILL HERE...

...AND IT COULD STILL BE DANGEROUS!

SIGNAL EVERYBODY TA ADVANCE... REAL CAREFUL LIKE.

LOOK, SIR! THERE'S SOMEBODY ELSE CRAWLING OUT OF THE SHIP!

HOLD YER FIRE! IF THAT'S WHO I THINK IT IS, WE COULD ALL BE IN BIG TROUBLE!

MY CANE IS GONE! AND SOMEHOW I KNOW THAT THAT ALIEN IS RESPONSIBLE.

BUT THE ATMOSPHERE, THE STORM! ODIN WAS HERE!

HIS PRESENCE STILL LINGERS! AND HE DID NOT TAKE ME!

ONLY A FEW HOURS AGO, I NEARLY ENVIED THE MORTALS AROUND ME!

AND NOW, I MAY HAVE TO JOIN THEM... FOREVER!

FATHER! HEAR ME!

DO NOT FORSAKE ME HERE!

NEXT--A FOOL AND HIS HAMMER...

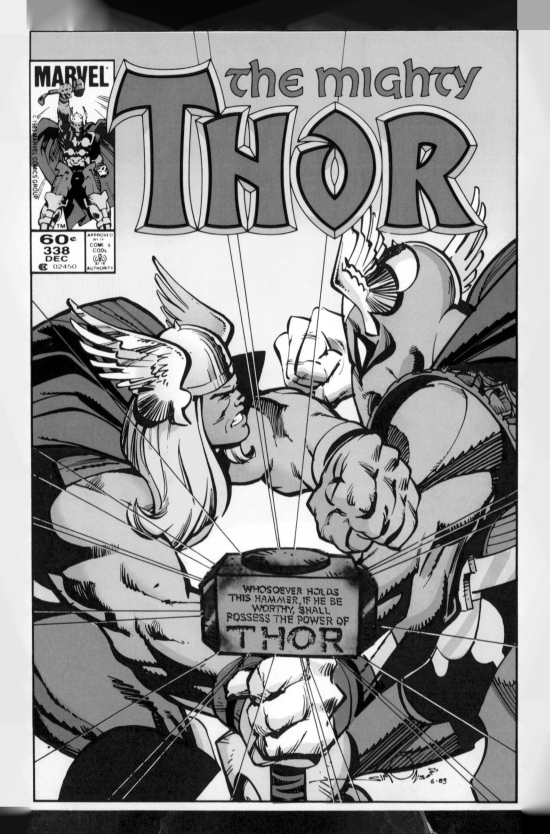

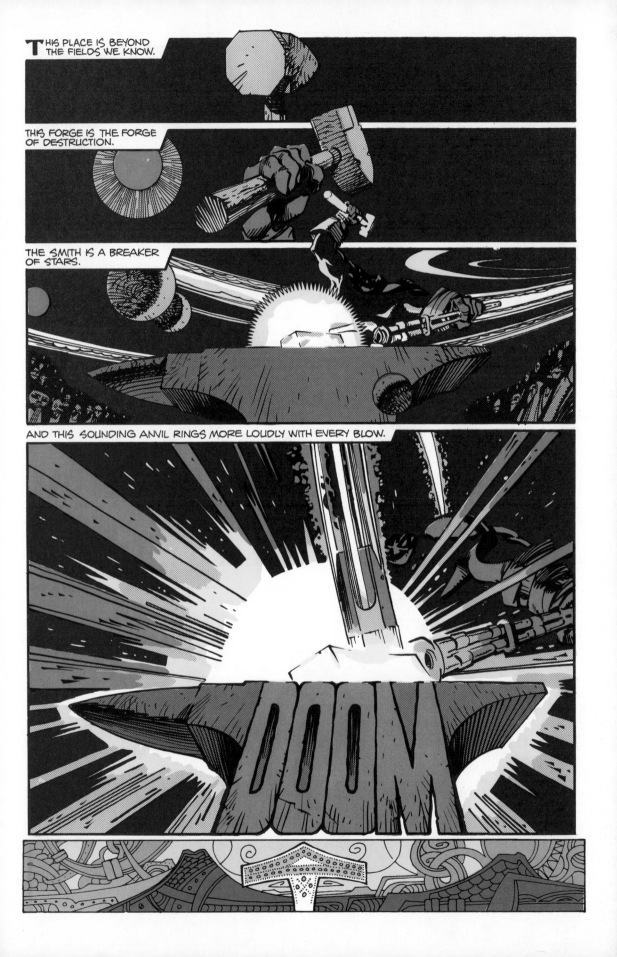

STAN LEE PRESENTS: the MIGHTY THOR®

ORDINARILY, DR. DONALD BLAKE CAN SIMPLY TAP HIS ENCHANTED CANE AND BE TRANSFORMED INTO THE MIGHTY THOR, AS THE CANE BECOMES HIS MIGHTY HAMMER, MJOLNIR.

BUT THE HAMMER HAS BEEN CARRIED OFF BY THOR'S RECENT FOE, BETA RAY BILL, WHO WAS HIMSELF TRANSFORMED BY THE MAGIC WEAPON...

...LEAVING A DESPERATE DONALD BLAKE STRANDED ON EARTH, TRAPPED WITHIN HIS MORTAL IDENTITY...

ODIN! FATHER ODIN!

HEAR ME!

A FOOL AND HIS HAMMER...

HEAR ME.

IT'S NO USE. THE HAMMER'S GONE AND WITHOUT IT, I'M DOOMED TO REMAIN A MORTAL, UNABLE TO CONTACT ASGARD OR ODIN, MY FATHER.

WHAT WILL I DO? WHAT WILL I DO? ODIN, HELP ME.

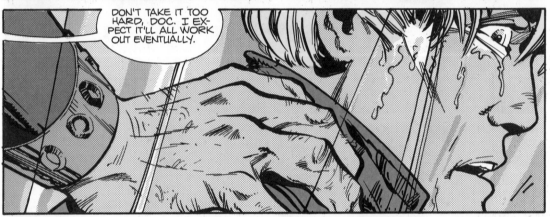

DON'T TAKE IT TOO HARD, DOC. I EXPECT IT'LL ALL WORK OUT EVENTUALLY.

COLONEL FURY! I... I SHOULD HAVE KNOWN YOU'D BE HERE.

I'VE LOST EVERYTHING, NICK! THERE WAS AN ALIEN ON BOARD THIS SHIP. WE FOUGHT AND I TURNED BACK INTO DON BLAKE AT THE WRONG MOMENT.

HE KNOCKED ME OUT AND NOW IT LOOKS AS THOUGH HE'S TAKEN MY HAMMER. THAT'S NEVER HAPPENED BEFORE. AND WITHOUT MJOLNIR, I'M MAROONED HERE, PERHAPS FOREVER.

MAYBE NOT, DOC. AN OLD GUY WITH ONE EYE APPEARED AND THEN VANISHED, TAKING THE ALIEN WITH HIM.

SURE THING, DOC. SHIELD'S BEEN TRACKIN' THIS SHIP ALL THE WAY. THOUGHT YA MIGHT NEED A LITTLE HELP WHEN IT CRASHED ON EARTH.

LOOKS LIKE WE WERE RIGHT. YOU OKAY?

IF THAT WAS YER OLD MAN, HE AIN'T GONNA BE REAL HAPPY TO SEE SOMEBODY ELSE WEARIN' YER THREADS AND HEFTIN' YER HAMMER.

'TIS THOR!

LORD ODIN HAS RECALLED HIM FROM MIDGARD.*

TRULY ONLY HE CAN HELP US NOW IN THIS, OUR HOUR OF NEED.

*EARTH.

BACK, DEMONS! YOU'VE MORE TRICKS ABOUT YOU THAN I DREAMED OF BUT IT WILL AVAIL YOU NAUGHT!

WHO... WHO ARE YOU THAT WEARS THE COSTUME AND CARRIES THE HAMMER OF THE MIGHTY THOR?

NO ASGARDIAN COULD EVEN LIFT THE ENCHANTED MALLET, LET ALONE DEFEAT THOR IN BATTLE.

IT IS NOT FOR YOU TO QUESTION ME! TELL ME RATHER WHERE THIS PLACE IS... AND WHO YOU DEMONS SERVE.

BETA RAY BILL'S ONSLAUGHT IS DEADLY AND OVER-WHELMING! BUT THE SHOCK OF THE ATTACK SCARCE-LY EQUALS THE ASGARDIAN'S SUBSEQUENT SURPRISE!

STRIKE NOT YOUR CREATOR NOR RETURN TO THIS FALSE MASTER!

WHERE IS THOR?

WHERE IS MY SON?

I KNOW NOT WHO YOU MEAN!

BUT I FAIRLY WON THE HAMMER IN COMBAT AND NOT ALL YOUR POWER CAN CHANGE THAT!

YOUR VOICE HAS THE RING OF TRUTH!

LET ME STAY MY WRATH A MOMENT AND SEEK TO KNOW MORE OF THIS MATTER.

EVEN THOR'S PRODIGIOUS STRENGTH WOULD BE HARD PUT TO SHATTER A VESSEL OF ETHEREAL FORCE.

AND NOW WE SHALL LEARN WHAT WE MUST, NO MATTER THE COST!

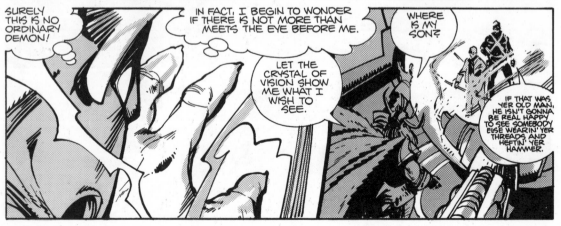

SURELY THIS IS NO ORDINARY DEMON!

IN FACT, I BEGIN TO WONDER IF THERE IS NOT MORE THAN MEETS THE EYE BEFORE ME.

LET THE CRYSTAL OF VISION SHOW ME WHAT I WISH TO SEE.

WHERE IS MY SON?

IF THAT WAS YER OLD MAN, HE ISN'T GONNA BE REAL HAPPY TO SEE SOMEBODY ELSE WEARIN' YER THREADS AND HEFTIN' YER HAMMER.

FACT IS, I'M SURPRISED HE HASN'T...

IS IT MY IMAGINATION OR IS IT GETTIN' DARKER?

I HOPE IT WASN'T SOMETHIN' I SAID.

BARROOM

YEOW! NOT AGAIN!

NOW DOC'S GONE, TOO. BROTHER, THIS IS GONNA MAKE ONE HECK OF A REPORT!

WELL, GOOD LUCK, BLAKE. I THINK YER GONNA NEED IT.

IT LOOKS LIKE IT'S STARTIN' TO RAIN AGAIN, TOO.

SWELL. DON'T THESE GUYS EVER TRAVEL IN DRY WEATHER?

AT THAT MOMENT, ON ASGARD...

FATHER!

WELCOME HOME, MY SON. HOW STANDS THY ZEST FOR ADVENTURE NOW?

UNABATED, MY LORD, THOUGH I CONFESS THAT A MOMENT AGO, I FEARED THAT PERHAPS ALL MY ADVENTURES WERE OVER.

AH, MY YOUTHFUL SON, DOES THIS MEAN THAT YOUR MORTAL FRIEND HAS MORE FAITH IN A ONE-EYED VISION THAN MY BOY HAS IN HIS OWN FATHER?

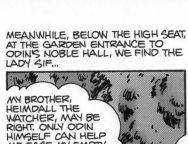

MEANWHILE, BELOW THE HIGH SEAT, AT THE GARDEN ENTRANCE TO ODIN'S NOBLE HALL, WE FIND THE LADY SIF...

MY BROTHER, HEIMDALL THE WATCHER, MAY BE RIGHT. ONLY ODIN HIMSELF CAN HELP ME EASE MY EMPTY HEART NOW THAT THOR AND I ARE NO LONGER PROMISED TO EACH OTHER.

WOULD THAT ODIN HAD NEVER GIVEN THOR HIS MORTAL IDENTITY SO LONG AGO. I STILL LOVE THE NOBLE WARRIOR BUT HIS HEART MAY EVER BE DIVIDED BETWEEN ASGARD AND MIDGARD.

AND THOUGH MY LOVE SURPASSES UNDERSTANDING, I CANNOT SHARE THOR'S JOY FOR EARTH.

BUT WHAT'S THIS I HEAR?

SURELY MY SENSES DECEIVE ME!

AH, LADY LORELEI, TO FEEL YOUR ARMS ENTWINED ABOUT ME, YOUR SWEET BREATH UPON MY FACE, YOUR LIPS PRESSED TO MINE... 'TIS ALL THAT I DESIRE.

FOR SUCH KISSES, I WOULD FORSAKE EVEN MIDGARD ITSELF!

SO.

I... UH... I... MILADY SIF?

THOUGH MY OWN BREATH IS LESS SWEET, MY LORD THOR, ACCEPT THIS PARTING KISS...

THE KISS OF A WARRIOR BORN AND NO SOFT PLAYTHING!

AS FOR YOU, YOU BAWD, I LEAVE THOR TO YOUR TENDER EMBRACES! BUT HAVE A CARE!

FALSE HEART ONCE IS FALSE HEART FOREVER!

SPUTTER SPUT

HAHAHA! WHAT A RARE JEST! A WONDERFUL FOLLY!

AH, LORELEI, I WOULD HOLD YOU IN MY ARMS FOREVER FOR SUCH SPORT AS THIS.

PERHAPS, MY LORD, I WOULD NOT HAVE UNDERTAKEN THIS JEST HAD I KNOWN BEFOREHAND THAT IT WOULD BE SO DANGEROUS!

NONSENSE!

THE LADY SIF WILL NOW SHORTLY DEPART THIS IMMORTAL SPHERE.

AND YOU, MY SWEETLING...

...MAY YET SUCCEED WHERE YOUR SISTER, THE ENCHANTRESS...

...HAS EVER FAILED.

BUT EVEN AS LOKI CHORTLES IN HIS GLEE, WE RETURN TO THE HIGH SEAT AND ITS OCCUPANTS...

LISTEN WELL THEN, LORDS, AND I WILL TELL MY TALE, THE STORY OF BETA RAY BILL.

MINE IS AN ANCIENT AND NOBLE RACE THAT HAS LIVED IN THE HEART OF A GALAXY FROM TIME IMMEMORIAL.

WE BUILT OUR CITIES IN THE BURNING SKIES AND DANCED IN THE SUNLIGHT.

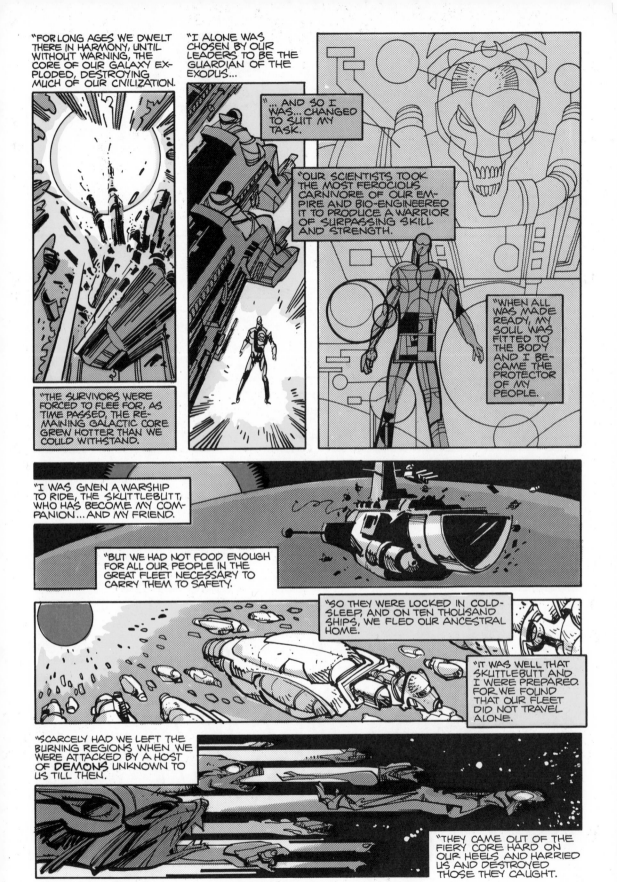

"FOR LONG AGES WE DWELT THERE IN HARMONY, UNTIL WITHOUT WARNING, THE CORE OF OUR GALAXY EXPLODED, DESTROYING MUCH OF OUR CIVILIZATION.

"I ALONE WAS CHOSEN BY OUR LEADERS TO BE THE GUARDIAN OF THE EXODUS...

"...AND SO I WAS... CHANGED TO SUIT MY TASK.

"OUR SCIENTISTS TOOK THE MOST FEROCIOUS CARNIVORE OF OUR EMPIRE AND BIO-ENGINEERED IT TO PRODUCE A WARRIOR OF SURPASSING SKILL AND STRENGTH.

"THE SURVIVORS WERE FORCED TO FLEE FOR, AS TIME PASSED, THE REMAINING GALACTIC CORE GREW HOTTER THAN WE COULD WITHSTAND.

"WHEN ALL WAS MADE READY, MY SOUL WAS FITTED TO THE BODY AND I BECAME THE PROTECTOR OF MY PEOPLE.

"I WAS GIVEN A WARSHIP TO RIDE, THE SKUTTLEBUTT, WHO HAS BECOME MY COMPANION... AND MY FRIEND.

"BUT WE HAD NOT FOOD ENOUGH FOR ALL OUR PEOPLE IN THE GREAT FLEET NECESSARY TO CARRY THEM TO SAFETY.

"SO THEY WERE LOCKED IN COLD-SLEEP, AND ON TEN THOUSAND SHIPS, WE FLED OUR ANCESTRAL HOME.

"IT WAS WELL THAT SKUTTLEBUTT AND I WERE PREPARED, FOR WE FOUND THAT OUR FLEET DID NOT TRAVEL ALONE.

"SCARCELY HAD WE LEFT THE BURNING REGIONS WHEN WE WERE ATTACKED BY A HOST OF DEMONS UNKNOWN TO US TILL THEN.

"THEY CAME OUT OF THE FIERY CORE HARD ON OUR HEELS AND HARRIED US AND DESTROYED THOSE THEY CAUGHT.

"SKUTTLEBUTT AND I FOUGHT THEM UNTIL OUR PEOPLE HAD DRAWN AWAY SAFELY. THEN WE FLED AND ESCAPED BUT THE DEMONS TURNED AND FOLLOWED US.

"I SPED ON AHEAD OF THE FLEET, SEARCHING FOR SANCTUARY AND FINDING NONE.

THE PURSUIT STILL GOES ON ACROSS COUNTLESS LIGHT-YEARS. THEY ARE SLOWLY OVERTAKING US BUT WE CANNOT FIND A HAVEN.

NOW I HAVE FOUND A WEAPON THAT MAY PROTECT MY PEOPLE FOR ALL TIME, AND I AM LOATHE TO GIVE IT UP.

ESPECIALLY AS I HAVE WON IT IN FAIR COMBAT.

WHAT?

I SAY THEE **NAY**, NOBLE WARRIOR.

IT WAS **NOT** THOR THOU DID DEFEAT BUT A MORTAL SHELL! I--!

BE STILL, MY SON. HE HAS A POINT.

YET, TRULY, MIGHTY BILL, THE COMBAT YOU SPEAK OF WAS NOT ENTIRELY FAIR.

FOR MY SON FOUGHT UNDER THE HANDICAP OF A SPELL THAT I MY-SELF CREATED MANY YEARS AGO, BOUND UP IN THIS VERY HAMMER.

IN THOSE DAYS, THOR WAS PROUD AND HEADSTRONG. I SOUGHT TO TEACH HIM THE WISDOM OF PATIENCE.

IN MY OWN PRIDE, I FASHIONED A MAGIC ABOUT THE HAMMER.

AN INSTANT LATER, THOR MATERIALIZES ABOVE A FORBIDDING LANDSCAPE...

SKARTHEIM! WHERE EVEN GODS MAY PERISH!

MY FATHER SURELY HAS ENTRUSTED OUR FATES TO THE NORNS* THEMSELVES!

*THE THREE FATES!

BUT I DO NOT SEE MY OPPONENT.

NO DOUBT LORD ODIN CAUSED HIM TO APPEAR ELSEWHERE IN THIS DANGEROUS REALM.

I FEEL THE HEAT OF THE EARTH ITSELF!

THE VERY GROUND ERUPTS BENEATH MY FEET!

I MUST TAKE MYSELF TO A SAFER PERCH!

UHGG!

NAY, THUNDER GOD, THERE IS NO SAFETY IN ALL THIS LAND AS LONG AS ONE OF US REMAINS ALIVE!

RASH WARRIOR! SO BOOTLESS AN ATTACK UPON A PRINCE OF ASGARD WILL SCARCELY WIN YOU THE HAMMER!

NOT EVEN WHEN THE PRINCE WILL CUSHION OUR DEADLY PLUNGE FROM THE CLIFFS WITH HIS OWN BODY?

KRAKS!

WHAT? DO YOU SUPPOSE A SIMPLE FALL WILL INJURE ME? THOUGH I AM WITHOUT THE GODLY POWER OF MY HERITAGE, I DO POSSESS THE STRENGTH THAT IS MY BIRTHRIGHT!

STILL I AM STRONG ENOUGH TO GIVE THEE PAUSE.

BUT PAUSE IS NOT A VICTORY, THUNDERER!

AND VICTORY WILL SOON BE MINE!

THOUGH I DO GRIEVE TO DO THIS DEED, YOUR OWN FATHER HAS COMMANDED IT.

HIS WILL BE DONE!

NOT EVERYONE IN ASGARD, HOWEVER, IS ATTENDING THE MIGHTY HALL OF ODIN TO WITNESS THIS TITANIC STRUGGLE. ELSEWHERE IN THE DESERTED BOULEVARDS OF THE GOLDEN CITY...

BALDER, MY FRIEND, I FEAR YOU DO NOT PROPERLY APPRECIATE THE TRUE PHILOSOPHY OF EATING!

TAKE ME, FOR INSTANCE. SOME SAY I EAT BECAUSE I HAVE A WIFE WHO COULD SINK A LONGSHIP AND EIGHTEEN SCREAMING OFF-SPRING WHOSE FURY WOULD DAUNT NOBLE ODIN HIMSELF!

SCURRILOUS LIES! I EAT BECAUSE I ENJOY IT. IT IS POSSIBLY THE GREATEST PLEASURE IN LIFE! AND ONE OF THE FEW I HAVE LEFT, IF I MAY SAY SO.

BUT NOBLE FRIEND, EATING SHOULD BE AN AFFIRMATION OF LIFE, NOT AN ESCAPE FROM IT.

SHOULD YOU NOT TASTE MORE KEENLY THE JOYS OF LIVING, BALDER, YOU WHO ALONE AMONG US HAS TASTED DEATH ITSELF?

ONE WOULD THINK SO, VOLSTAGG, MY FRIEND.

BUT THE VISIONS I HAVE SEEN TROUBLE ME CEASE-LESSLY.

THE FACES OF THOSE I HAVE SLAIN IN HONORABLE COMBAT ARE NOW MORE REAL TO ME THAN THE BRIGHT BLUE SKIES OF ASGARD.

AND THE SAVOR OF LIVING SEEMS FOREVER DUST TO ME NOW. AN EMPTY DREAM.

THEN PERHAPS THE DREAMER SHOULD RETURN TO HIS FINAL REST!

EH? WHO--?

I AM AGNAR, SON OF HROTHGAR! I HAVE COME FROM VANAHEIM SEEKING BALDER, WHOSE FAME TELLS OF HIS PROWESS IN BATTLE.

I WOULD CHALLENGE HIM TO FIGHT IF HE BE NOT A COWARD...

...AND PROVE TO ME THAT HE IS A BETTER WARRIOR THAN I!

NAY, AGNAR, I AM DONE WITH FIGHTING. I'LL FIGHT NO MORE FOREVER.

SPURN ME, WILL YOU? THEN DIE WHERE YOU STAND! I'LL... HUH?

WHAT TRICKERY IS THIS THAT ALLOWED YOU TO ESCAPE MY BLOW?

COME BACK! I'LL NOT LET YOU WALK AWAY AS THOUGH I WERE SOME THRALL!

COME BACK! OR BY THE MOTHER THAT BORE ME, I'LL SPLIT YOU WHERE YOU STAND!

HOLD, MY YOUNG FRIEND. PERMIT ME TO SPEAK ON BEHALF OF THE NOBLE BALDER.

OWW! MY FOOT! GET OFF, YOU CLUMSY OAF!

TUT, TUT, AGNAR, I AM BEYOND SUCH INSULTS! IN FACT, TO DEMONSTRATE MY GENEROUS NATURE, LET ME SHOW YOU SOME OF THE WONDERS OF THE ETERNAL REALM WHILE BALDER CONTINUES HIS WALK.

NO. I WANT TO... OW, MY FOOT! I THINK IT'S BROKEN!

I AM OLDER THAN YOU, AGNAR. OLDER THAN BALDER. AND IN HIS PRIME, BRAVE VOLSTAGG FOUGHT BESIDE MANY FAMOUS FIGHTERS! BUT NEVER HAVE I BEHELD A MORE COURAGEOUS, MORE GENTLE WARRIOR THAN BALDER THE BRAVE.

HERE'S A SHADY SPOT.

CRUNCH!

SURELY THOSE OF VANAHEIM ARE MADE OF STERNER STUFF. ALLOW ME TO CARRY YOU. WE'LL VISIT THE PALACE GARDENS. VERY SOOTHING AND WE CAN CONVERSE THERE AT OUR LEISURE.

OOF!

HIS DEEDS ARE LEGENDARY-- THE SLAYING OF THE UTGARD DRAGON, THE BINDING OF THORN OF THE FOUR RINGS-- THE SAVING OF ASGARD A HUNDRED TIMES! NOW ALL THAT HAS CHANGED-- PERHAPS FOREVER!

OFF! GET OFF!

PATIENCE, LITTLE ONE. YOU FEEL YOU'RE BRAVE ENOUGH TO FACE DEATH, DO YOU? WELL, BALDER IS THE ONLY GOD AMONG US WHO HAS HIMSELF DIED AND RETURNED TO TELL THE TALE...

...AND A BLOOD-CHILLING TALE IT IS, TOO! JUST THE SORT OF STORY FOR A SUMMER'S AFTERNOON.

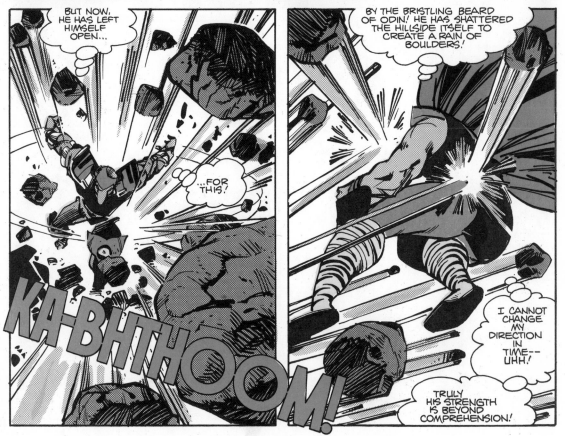

STILL, I AM PROVIDED WITH A WEAPON THAT MAY SERVE ME AS WELL AS THE HAMMER OVER WHICH WE FIGHT!

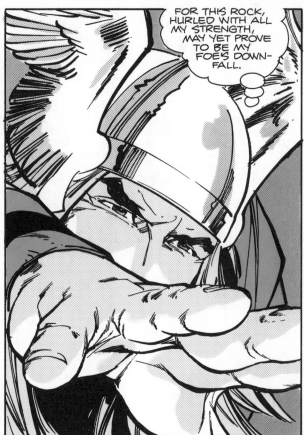

FOR THIS ROCK, HURLED WITH ALL MY STRENGTH, MAY YET PROVE TO BE MY FOE'S DOWNFALL.

BTHOUUM!

I'M FALLING INTO THE RIVER OF LAVA! CAN THIS BE THE END OF MY QUEST?

BUT WAIT! THERE! THAT RAFT OF OBSIDIAN! IF ONLY I CAN TWIST MYSELF AROUND IN TIME--!

SAVED! YET EVEN NOW, MY FOE LEAPS UPON ME! SURELY, I MUST GIRD MYSELF, FOR THE SUPREME MOMENT IS AT HAND!

MERE WORDS CANNOT DESCRIBE THE POWER OF THE BLOWS AS BOTH COMBATANTS UNLEASH THEIR FULL FURY IN ONE FINAL CATACLYSMIC EFFORT!

THE BLAST LEVELS THE SURROUNDING COUNTRYSIDE...

...TIME IS FROZEN IN THE INSTANT...

...AND ALL OF NATURE SEEMS TO HOLD ITS BREATH...

...UNTIL BOTH WARRIORS LIE QUIETLY SIDE-BY-SIDE...

...AS THEIR OBSIDIAN RAFT FLOATS DOWN THE RIVER OF LAVA TOWARD A SPECTACULAR DESTRUCTION!

FINALLY...

I...I LIVE! THE HEAT REVIVES ME. YET I AM BROKEN INSIDE. I FEEL IT.

THOR LIES UNCONSCIOUS STILL. I HAVE BUT TO LEAP TO THE SHORE AND SAFETY AND THE HAMMER IS WON!

QUICKLY-- THE FALLS ARE JUST AHEAD!

NO! MY FOE IS TOO BRAVE TO PERISH SO MEANLY IN THIS FORSAKEN WILDERNESS.

I...UGH...I MUST CARRY US BOTH TO SAFETY.

TOO LATE! THE RAFT ALREADY PLUNGES O'ER THE FIERY BRINK! BUT I MUST TRY!

AND WITH A FINAL GROAN, BETA RAY BILL LEAPS FOR THE SHORE...

...ONLY TO BE ENVELOPED BY A BLINDING FLASH OF ENERGY...

...THAT TRANSPORTS HIM IN THE WINK OF AN EYE TO THE GLEAMING HALLS OF ASGARD BEFORE A SHOCKED AND SILENT GATHERING.

THE HAMMER... IS MINE!

LORD ODIN, YOUR SON YET LIVES. THE FINEST FOE I HAVE EVER FOUGHT. BUT I HAVE BESTED HIM.

NEXT-SOMETHING OLD, SOMETHING NEW...!

BETTER STOCK UP ON COPIES, KIDS! THIS ONE'LL BE A COLLECTOR'S ITEM FOR SURE.?

STAN LEE PRESENTS: the MIGHTY THOR

MOMENTS AGO, BETA RAY BILL, A BIONIC ALIEN, BESTED THE MIGHTY THOR IN SINGLE COMBAT AND SO WON THE RIGHT TO POSSESS THOR'S ENCHANTED HAMMER, MJOLNIR.*

BUT EVEN AS HE ANNOUNCES HIS VICTORY BEFORE THE STUNNED ASGARDIANS...

SOMETHING OLD, SOMETHING NEW...

UGGHG...

*AS SEEN IN OUR LAST COUPLE OF ISSUES.

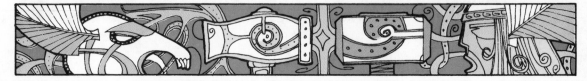

...AND FOR A LONG MOMENT, THERE IS SILENCE!

AROUSE YOURSELVES! LET THE IMPERIAL GUARD CARRY BOTH COMBATANTS TO THE HOUSE OF HEALING WITHOUT DELAY! AND BID THE ROYAL PHYSICIANS APPLY ALL THEIR ARTS!

THESE BRAVE WARRIORS MUST **NOT** PERISH!

BUT THOUGH THE ARMS OF **HELA,** THE DEATH GODDESS, BECKON TO EACH, NEITHER THOR NOR BETA RAY BILL IS DESTINED TO SURRENDER TO HER EMBRACE THIS DAY.

FOR THE SKILLS OF ODIN'S PHYSICIANS ARE UNMATCHED IN ALL THE NINE WORLDS.

STILL, THE HEROES' HURTS ARE GRIEVOUS AND EACH RESTS QUIETLY UNDER THE WATCHFUL (AND CURIOUS) EYES OF THEIR ATTENDANTS.

THE ALIEN SLEEPS PEACEFULLY.

BUT HE IS A STRANGE MIXTURE OF STRENGTH AND SORROW. THOUGH HE HAS WON THE HAMMER, HE TAKES NO JOY IN HIS VICTORY.

THEY SAY BILL REGAINS HIS STRENGTH AS QUICKLY AS THE MIGHTY THOR. DO YOU SUPPOSE HE WILL REMAIN LONG IN ASGARD?

I FOR ONE WOULD BE INTERESTED TO LEARN JUST HOW MECHANICAL HE REALLY IS.

WELL, I FOR ONE COULD CARE LESS. I'VE SEEN HIM...

...AND HE'S REPULSIVE!

I'D SOONER KISS A DOG THAN BE IN THE SAME ROOM WITH HIM!

RECALLING SOME PAST TRIUMPH, LORELEI?

THOR IS NO DOG, BUT THE HANDSOMEST GOD IN ALL ASGARD, LADY SIF, AND AFTER THIS DEFEAT, HE MAY WELCOME SUCH COMFORT AS ONLY I CAN GIVE.

HANDSOME IS AS HANDSOME DOES. BILL HAS LIFTED THE HAMMER AND FOUGHT AGAINST THOR AS NO ONE EVER HAS BEFORE. TO SEE LESS THAN THAT IS TO MIS-TAKE HIM.

THEN PER-HAPS **YOU** SHOULD EMBRACE THE ALIEN! HE MIGHT WEL-COME SUCH COMFORT AS YOU COULD GIVE.

AND WITH THAT, LORELEI LEAVES, UNAWARE OF THE WATCHING EYE THAT SEES ALL THINGS...

SOME, HOWEVER, ARE MORE PARTICULAR!

"SOME ARE MORE PARTICULAR!" FAGH!

PAY NO HEED TO HER, SIF. EVERY DOG HAS ITS DAY.

EVEN LORELEI.

BUT YOU MUST EXCUSE ME. I HAVE COME TO SEE OUR PATIENTS.

HOW FARES THE SON OF MY HEART?

DISGRACED BEFORE YOUR EYES, MY LORD.

I HAVE DECIDED. I WILL RENOUNCE MY GODHOOD AND LEAVE ASGARD FOR-EVER! NO LONGER AM I WORTHY TO BE THE GOD OF THUNDER!

YES, WELL...WE SHALL SEE. I THINK I OUGHT TO SPEAK WITH BILL.

HE IS NOT HAPPY ABOUT THE OUTCOME OF THIS BATTLE EITHER, I UNDER-STAND.

AS YOU WISH, FATHER, BUT TALKING WILL NOT CHANGE THE PAST.

MY MIND IS MADE UP. WHEN I AM WELL, I SHALL DEPART AND JOURNEY AMONG THE STARS.

ALL THINGS ARE POSSIBLE, MY SON.

PERHAPS DIS-CUSSION MAY BE ABLE TO HELP US WHERE BRUTE STRENGTH SEEMS TO HAVE FAILED.

LORD ODIN, I AM HONORED. AND GRATEFUL. YOUR PHYSICIANS AND YOUR SMITHS HAVE WORKED WONDERS. I AM NEARLY HEALED. HOW IS YOUR SON?

WELL ENOUGH, THANK YOU. ALL THINGS CONSIDERED.

AND YOU? THE GOSSIP OF THE HOUSE TELLS OF YOUR SINGULAR LACK OF ENTHUSIASM CONCERNING YOUR VICTORY.

I AM DEEPLY TROUBLED, MY LORD. FOR MYSELF AND MY PEOPLE, THEY NEED THE POWER OF THE HAMMER DESPERATELY. BUT MY HEART MISGIVES ME.

THOUGH I HAVE WON THIS BATTLE, IS MY CLAIM TO THE HAMMER'S POWER ESTABLISHED FOREVER, OR ONLY UNTIL I, MYSELF, MEET SOME STRONGER CHALLENGER?

THE HAMMER WAS FORGED IN THE BEGINNING OF TIME TO BE CARRIED BY THOR ALONE. MY VICTORY DOES NOT ALTER THAT, NOR PERMIT ME TO FORGET IT.

AND, IN TRUTH, I COULD NOT BRING MYSELF TO SLAY THOR, ALTHOUGH SUCH WAS THE ESTABLISHED CONDITION OF THE CONTEST.

YOU ARE A HIGH AND PUISSANT LORD. IS THERE NO WAY OUT OF THIS DILEMMA OF HONOR AND NEED?

YOU HAVE BUT TO ASK.

CAN YOU... HELP ME?

IN THE PAST, IN RETURN FOR HELP, THE GODS DEMANDED A SACRIFICE. YOU HAVE ALREADY GIVEN ME SOMETHING MORE PRECIOUS THAN ANYTHING—THE LIFE OF MY SON.

THEREFORE, I WILL GIVE YOU WHAT AID I CAN. I SHALL BESTOW UPON YOU A GIFT THAT CARRIES AN AWESOME RESPONSIBILITY.

YOU HAVE PROVEN YOURSELF ABLE TO WIELD GREAT POWER AND WIELD IT WISELY. AND, YOU HAVE ASKED FOR HELP.

THE GIFT MAY YET SAVE YOUR PEOPLE... THE RESPONSIBILITY MIGHT DESTROY YOU!

THROOM BOOOM

IT IS DUSK WHEN A SOLITARY RIDER CRESTS THE DIVIDE THAT OVERLOOKS NIDAVELLIR, THE REALM OF THE DWARFS...

EITRI, LOOK! SOMEONE HAS CROSSED THE FORBIDDEN PATH THROUGH THE MOUNTAINS OF ULLTHANG!

GREETINGS, NOBLE DWARFS.

EVENING COMES ON AND THIS WANDERER HAS JOURNEYED FAR. MIGHT I SHARE YOUR FIRE AND FELLOWSHIP THIS NIGHT? YOU'LL FIND ME A GENIAL COMPANION.

WEL- COME, **MOST HIGH.** PLEASE ACCEPT OUR HOSPITALITY.

YOU KNOW ME, EITRI?

HAD I BUT ONE EYE, LORD ODIN, I SHOULD RECOGNIZE YOUR MANTLED POWER EVEN IN THE DARK.

AND I WOULD KNOW THAT YOU HAD SOUGHT ME OUT FOR A PURPOSE, NOT MERELY TO SHARE A FIRE.

WHAT DOES THE LORD OF ASGARD SEEK IN NIDAVELLIR?

YOUR SKILL, EITRI. FOR A TASK THAT ONLY YOU CAN PERFORM.

COME THEN. SIT BESIDE ME AND TELL ME WHAT THE DWARFS CAN DO FOR THE GODS.

YOU ASK MUCH, LORD ODIN. MORE THAN WE DWARFS CAN EASILY GIVE.

IF THE TASK WERE SIMPLE, EITRI, I WOULD NOT HAVE SOUGHT OUT THE GREATEST OF ALL DWARF SMITHS.

SO YOU SAY!

LONG AGO, WE DWARFS WERE HUMBLED AND DRIVEN FROM THE LIGHT BY THE GODS!

WE LIVE NOW BENEATH THE GROUND AND SEEK OUT THE EARTH'S TREASURES, BUT WE HAVE NOT FORGOTTEN OLD HURTS AND OUR HEARTS ARE BITTER.

YET THE GODS ALSO GAVE US OUR FORM AND OUR THOUGHTS.

SO WE WILL DO THIS NEW TASK YOU SET US BUT ON ONE CONDITION AND ONE CONDITION ONLY.

WE HAVE A CHAMPION AMONG US NOW, A MIGHTY FIGHTER.

SEND US A WOMAN WHO CAN DEFEAT HIM AND WE WILL DO THIS THING YOU ASK. BUT IF SHE LOSES, SHE MUST REMAIN WITH THE DWARFS FOREVER, TO SERVE OUR CHAMPION AS HIS CHATTEL!

THUS DO WE REPAY THE GODS FOR ANCIENT WRONGS!

BUT AS SIF PASSES THROUGH ASGARD'S GOLDEN GATES, THE COMING BATTLE IS ONLY ONE OF MANY THOUGHTS THAT SPIN THROUGH HER MIND...

...AS SHE SEES AGAIN HER MEETING WITH THE ALL-FATHER THAT VERY MORNING.

SUCH WAS MY BARGAIN, SIF. THE DWARFS WANT A GODDESS TO FIGHT THEIR CHAMPION AND I KNOW THAT YOU HAVE SOUGHT DISTRACTION TO EASE YOUR HEART'S ACHE.

BUT I DO NOT COMMAND THIS THING.

THE DECISION RESTS WITH YOU.

MY LORD, 'TIS TRUE I AM EMPTY AND THOUGHT THAT BATTLE WOULD FILL MY NEED.

NOW, FOR REASONS OF MY OWN, I WOULD GLADLY TRAVEL TO HELA'S PALLID DOMAIN ITSELF TO DEMONSTRATE MY PROWESS.

VERY WELL, CHILD. ARM THY-SELF STRONGLY AND KNOW THAT I SHALL BE WATCHING OVER YOU FROM AFAR.

AND AS HER THOUGHTS RETURN TO THE PRESENT...

I DARED NOT TELL EVEN ODIN THAT I RIDE NOW EAGER TO BATTLE BE-CAUSE OF A DESIRE SO SECRET THAT NONE MUST KNOW. I CAN SCARCELY BELIEVE IT MYSELF.

THERE IS ANOTHER WARRIOR IN THIS WORLD WHO IS AS BRAVE, AS VALIANT AS THE MIGHTY THOR!

AND THOUGH HE WEARS A GUISE AS ALIEN AS ANY I HAVE EVER SEEN, STILL I WOULD FIND FAVOR IN HIS EYES.

STILL I WOULD SHOW HIM THAT I, TOO, AM A WARRIOR BORN.

SO! THE CRAVEN ASGARDIANS HAVE DELIVERED A WIFE TO ME AT LAST AS I KNEW THEY WOULD! AND ABOUT TIME!

I KNEW THEY'D BE TOO AFRAID TO RESIST!

I MUST REMEMBER TO THANK EITRI!... EVENTUALLY!

NOW, MY PRETTY, BID FAREWELL TO THE SUN AND PREPARE TO LIVE WITH ME FOREVER IN THE DARK BENEATH THE AGELESS MOUNTAINS OF NIDAVELLIR.

OWWW!

THINK AGAIN, BRAGGART!

THE GODDESS HAS A STING, EH? NO MATTER!

NONE CAN OVER-COME THROGG THE DWARF!

BUT EVEN AS THROGG LEAPS HIGH INTO THE AIR ABOVE SIF, WE TURN ELSEWHERE TO FIND, IN THE GARDENS OF ASGARD, VOLSTAGG THE ENORMOUS CHATTING WITH AGNAR OF VANAHEIM...

MARK WELL THESE WORDS, MY YOUNG FRIEND, AND I WILL TELL THE STORY OF BALDER THE BRAVE AND HIS TRAGIC DEATH AS ONLY VOLSTAGG CAN!

FROM THIS CAUTIONARY TALE, YOU WILL LEARN MORE THAN YOU EVER WISHED TO ABOUT MUCH THAT IS HIDDEN EVEN FROM THE GODS.

"IT BEGAN WITH AN ARROW MAGICALLY CREATED BY THE ARCH DECEIVER LOKI, HIMSELF, MADE OF THE LITTLE PLANT MISTLETOE. AND ON A BLACK DAY FOR ASGARD, THAT ARROW SLEW BRAVE BALDER.

"THOUGH ANOTHER HELD THE BOW, LOKI WAS THE PERPETRATOR OF THE CRIME, AND HE WAS PUNISHED.

"BUT BALDER'S FATE WAS UN-KNOWN TO US, AND ONLY AFTER HE RETURNED TO THESE GOLDEN HALLS DID WE LEARN OF THE DREADFUL DESTINY THAT AWAITED HIM IN THE MISTS OF THE NIFFLEHEIM...

"...THE LAND OF HELA, GODDESS OF DEATH...

"...A DESTINY TO MAKE EVEN VALOROUS VOLSTAGG TREMBLE WITH FEAR."

ALAS, THE REST OF THE TALE MUST WAIT FOR WE JOURNEY NOW TO A PLACE BEYOND THE FIELDS WE KNOW, PERHAPS BEYOND THE NINE WORLDS THEMSELVES...

...TO WATCH AS A FIGURE WHO DWARFS THE STARS LOOMS OVER A MIGHTY ANVIL AND RAISES HIS SINEWED ARM HIGH ABOVE HIS HEAD.

AND EVEN OVER THE THUNDER OF HIS HAMMER, IF YOU LISTEN CAREFULLY, YOU CAN HEAR THE MURMUR OF THE HOST. AND THE MURMUR SAYS, "THE SWORD! THE SWORD!"

THE STORM IS RISING...

...AND THE ECHOES OF THE ANVIL RING ALL THE WAY TO EARTH. HERE, WE TURN TO LOOK UPON A LONELY LIGHTHOUSE IN THE PROVINCE OF QUEBEC IN CANADA...

INSIDE, WE FIND ITS SOLE OCCUPANT, A CROTCHETY OLD GENTLEMAN NAMED RENÉ BAROQUE.

BLINKITY-BLANK TRAVELING SALES-WOMAN!*

WHAT IN BLAZES AM I GONNA DO WITH THIS FOOD PROCESSOR SHE SOLD ME, EH? WHIP THESE BEANS TO DEATH?

JUST YOU WAIT'LL SHE SHOWS UP AGAIN! WHY, I'LL BET THEM EYELASHES WASN'T EVEN REAL. SHE'LL REGRET SHE EVER...

*TRANSLATED INTO THE VERNACULAR FROM THE FRENCH.

THUNK THUNK

WHAT'S THAT? SHE'S BACK ALREADY, EH? COULDN'T STAY AWAY! HA! NOW IT'S--

THUNK KACHUNK!

WAITAMINIT! THAT'S NO KNOCK! THE WHOLE BLASTED LIGHTHOUSE IS SHAKIN'! LEMME OUT'A HERE! LEMME--!

BUT RENÉ IS DESTINED NEVER TO REACH THE DOOR FOR AT THAT MOMENT THE VERY EARTH SPLITS ASUNDER...

FREE! FREE! AFTER ALL THE MILLENNIA! NOW AT LAST I WILL DESTROY THOSE WHO THOUGHT THEY HAD IMPRISONED ME FOREVER!

VENGEANCE WILL BE MINE!

HOLD STILL, WOMAN! YOU'RE NO MATCH FOR ME AND I DON'T WANT TO DAMAGE YOU!

BTHKASSH!

VERY THOUGHTFUL OF YOU. BUT SURELY YOU'D HAVE A BETTER CHANCE OF CATCHING ME IF YOU USED BOTH HANDS!

WHY NOT DROP THE CLUB?

GAAHHG!

MY HAND! YOU'VE CUT MY HAND!

ARE WE THROUGH OR DO YOU STILL THINK YOU CAN CATCH ME?

ROAARR!

SO YOU'VE DECIDED TO OUTTHINK ME AFTER ALL!

BE GRATEFUL THEN THAT I USE THE FLAT OF MY BLADE INSTEAD OF THE CUTTING EDGE!

WHOONK!

THE DWARFS HAVE CHOSEN A SINGULARLY INEPT CHAMPION IN THEIR CAUSE. BUT NO MATTER. THE BARGAIN IS COMPLETE AND THEY MUST FULFILL THEIR PART OF IT.

BUT WHAT DO I DO WITH THIS USELESS CREATURE? TO SLAY HIM WOULD SEEM ALMOST A WASTE OF TIME.

AND CERTAINLY NO LONGER NECESSARY, LADY SIF. IT IS THE LADY **SIF**, IS IT NOT? FOREMOST WARRIOR WOMAN AMONG THE ASGARDIANS. I HAD HOPED ODIN WOULD CHOOSE YOU TO FIGHT THROGG!

EITRI!

WHAT'S THIS? I HAVE DEFEATED YOUR CHAMPION. THE BARGAIN STANDS.

MOST CERTAINLY, VALIANT LADY. AND A GOOD BARGAIN IT WAS.

TOO LONG HAS THROGG LORDED OVER THE DWARFS, AIDED BY HIS FREAKISH SIZE, MAKING LIFE MISERABLE FOR MYSELF AND MY BROTHERS.

NOW, DEFEATED BY A WOMAN, HE'LL NOT SHOW HIS FACE AGAIN FOR AGES AND WE'LL BE RID OF HIS BULLYING WAYS.

WE DWARFS SHALL BE **HAPPY** TO AID LORD ODIN FOR THIS DELIVERANCE AND OUR CHILDREN WILL RELISH THE TALE OF MY BARGAIN WITH THE WANDERER.

RETURN TO YOUR LIEGE AND TELL HIM TO COME QUICKLY. WE SHALL BE READY ERE HE ARRIVES.

MAKE HASTE, LADS!

LEAP TO THE FIRES! STOKE THE FURNACES!

WE GO TO WORK!

SO SIF RETURNS TO ASGARD AND THE WORD GOES OUT FROM ODIN THAT HE AND THREE OTHERS WILL JOURNEY TO THE FORGES OF NIDAVELLIR...

...THERE TO PARTICIPATE IN A CREATION SUCH AS HAS NOT BEEN SEEN SINCE THE BEGINNING OF TIME.

BUT AS ALL IS MADE READY FOR THE TRIP WE FIND HIGH ATOP THE TOWERS OF ASGARD, TWO FIGURES DEEP IN CONVERSATION.

I AM WORRIED, LADY SIF, FOR MY PEOPLE. EVEN NOW, THEY MAY HAVE BEEN OVERTAKEN BY THE DEMONS THAT PURSUE THEIR FLEET. AND I AM HERE, UNABLE TO DEFEND THEM.

I THINK, BILL, THAT LORD ODIN HAS BEEN WATCHING OVER THEM.

IF ANY HARM HAD BEFALLEN THEM ERE NOW, WE WOULD KNOW.

THAT MAY BE, BUT MY PLACE IS WITH THEM AND AS I AM NOW FULLY RECOVERED, I LONG TO BE GONE FROM HERE.

IN THE GLORY OF ITS MANY BEAUTIES, ASGARD ONLY SERVES TO REMIND ME JUST HOW MUCH I HAVE GIVEN UP FOREVER.

IF... IF YOUR PEOPLE FIND SAFE HAVEN EVENTUALLY, WILL YOU EVER THINK OF RETURNING TO... US, SOMEDAY?

LOOK AT ME, LADY SIF. MY BROTHERS ARE THE BEASTS OF THE FORESTS, MY SISTERS THE MACHINES THAT DRIVE THE GREAT STARSHIPS.

WHEN I WAS REMADE AS A WARRIOR TO SAVE MY PEOPLE, I SURRENDERED ALL MY HUMANITY. I HAVE NONE LEFT... FOR ANYONE.

I DO NOT THINK I COULD BEAR THE PROSPECT OF RETURNING TO SUCH A PERFECT WORLD... NO MATTER HOW MUCH I MIGHT LONG TO.

THESE ARE THE **FURNACES** OF NIDAVELLIR, THE GREAT FORGES OF THE DWARFS, WHERE FOR AGES, THEY HAVE CREATED THE MOST WONDERFUL DELIGHTS OF THEIR IMAGINATIONS.

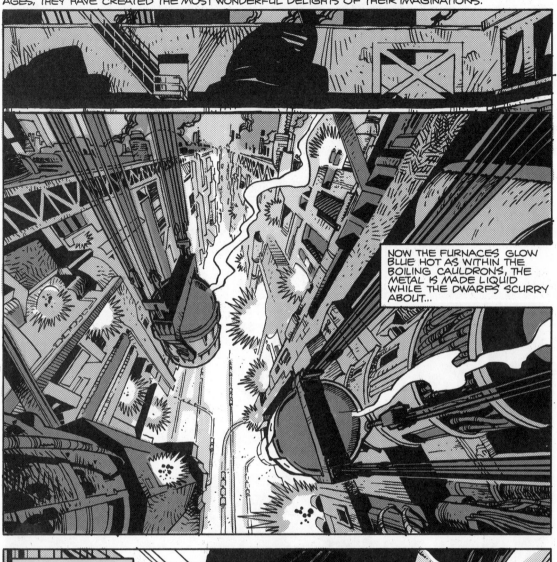

NOW THE FURNACES GLOW BLUE HOT AS WITHIN THE BOILING CAULDRONS, THE METAL IS MADE LIQUID WHILE THE DWARFS SCURRY ABOUT...

...AND THE FINAL PREPARATIONS ARE COMPLETED...

THE RAKING OF THE SLAG IS FINISHED. PREPARE TO TAP THE CHARGE!

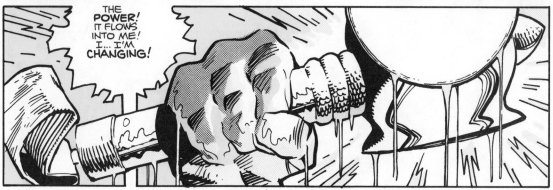

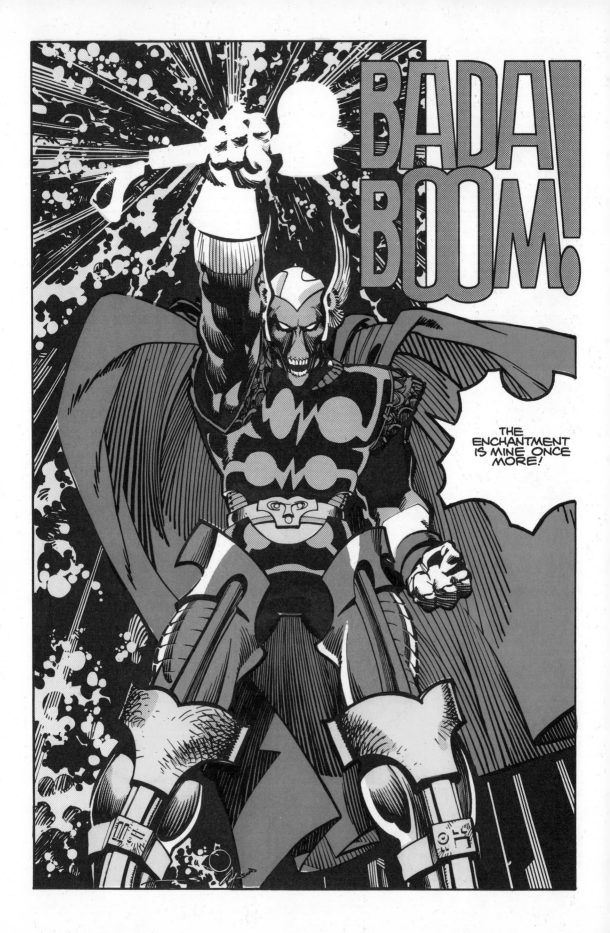

AND SO SHALL IT EVER BE FOR AS LONG AS YOU LIVE. THE FORGING IS COMPLETE.

BUT I MUST ASK YOU ONCE AGAIN, NOW THAT YOU FEEL THE POWER AND RESPONSIBILITY THAT YOU MUST SHOULDER, DO YOU TAKE THIS BURDEN OF YOUR OWN FREE WILL? FOR, ONCE UNDERTAKEN, IT WILL BE YOURS TO CARRY **FOREVER!**

I **DO** ACCEPT IT, WITH ALL MY HEART.

VERY WELL. THIS HAMMER SHALL BE CALLED **STORM BREAKER!** MAY YOU BEAR THE BURDEN AS WELL AS MY SON, WHO HAS CARRIED SUCH RESPONSIBILITY NEARLY ALL THE DAYS OF HIS LIFE.

AND NOW, THERE IS YET ONE FURTHER TASK TO DISCHARGE.

STEP FORWARD, THOR AND RECEIVE FROM MY HANDS THE HAMMER, MJOLNIR...

...WHICH IS NOW AND FOREVER **YOURS** ALONE!

CARRY IT AS YOU ALWAYS HAVE, WITH **HONOR!**

THERE IS NOT MUCH TIME. I MUST RETURN TO ASGARD FOR I AM WEARY AND SPENT FROM THE EFFORT OF THIS DAY.

BUT BEFORE WE LEFT THE GOLDEN REALM, I SAT IN THE HIGH SEAT AND SOUGHT OUT A VISION OF YOUR PEOPLE, BILL.

ARE THEY...?

YOU MUST MAKE HASTE. THE DEMONS ARE NEARLY UPON THEM AND EVEN NOW I FEAR IT MAY BE TOO LATE. BUT WITHOUT SUCH POWER AS YOU NOW POSSESS, YOU COULD NOT HAVE WITHSTOOD THEIR FURY.

FATHER, LET **ME** GO WITH HIM.

IF, AS YOU HAVE SAID, THE DEMONS' POWER RIVALS YOUR OWN, EVEN BILL MAY NOT SUCCEED AGAINST THEM.

YET **TOGETHER** WE MAY PREVAIL!

THIS WAS MY HOPE. BUT REMEMBER, MY SON, THE POWER OF THE DEMONS COMES FROM THEIR **SOURCE.** YOU MUST DESTROY IT OR THERE WILL BE **NO** VICTORY!

AND THEE, LADY?

FAREWELL, MY LIEGE! LOOK **NOT** FOR ME AGAIN TILL THE SUN STANDS UPON YON HILL!

SIF!

DO NOT TRY TO PREVENT ME, THOR. I HAVE **EARNED** THE RIGHT TO COME.

SO BE IT, AS THEY SAY.

LOOK TO THY WEAPONS, YOU DEMONS!

UP, TOOTHGNASHER! UP, TOOTHGRINDER! PULL FOR THE STARS! THE FOE AWAITS AND JOYOUS BATTLE IS BEFORE US!

THABAROOM!

NEXT: THOUGH HEL SHOULD BAR THE WAY!

STAN LEE PRESENTS: **the MIGHTY THOR**®

THOUGH HEL SHOULD BAR THE WAY!

THOR, SIF, AND BETA RAY BILL HAVE LEFT ASGARD FAR BEHIND AS THEY RIDE THE TIDES OF SPACE SEARCHING FOR BILL'S PEOPLE AND THE DEMONS WHO PURSUE THEM.

THE JOURNEY HAS BEEN LONG AND HAZARDOUS BUT AT LAST, THE FLEET OF STARSHIPS LIES LIKE A GREAT RIVER BELOW THEM...

RIDE ON! RIDE ON! ODIN SAID THAT ONLY BY DESTROYING THE SOURCE OF THESE DEMONS CAN WE WIN THE BATTLE!

I WILL REMAIN HERE AND PROTECT THE FLEET UNTIL YOU CAN REACH THE DEMON'S CRADLE AND SHATTER IT!

BUT, SIF...

RIDE ON! DO NOT WASTE WHAT LITTLE TIME WE HAVE! FOLLOW THE DEMONS HOME AND DO WHAT MUST BE DONE!

PROTECTING BILL'S PEOPLE IS MY DUTY!

WE CANNOT LEAVE HER THUS!

NO, SHE IS RIGHT. ONLY YOU AND I MIGHT WIN AGAINST THE DEMON HORDES ON THEIR OWN GROUND.

AND WE MUST LEARN ALL WE CAN ABOUT THEM SINCE EVEN MY FATHER, ODIN, CANNOT SEE INTO THEIR DOMAIN TO LEARN THEIR PURPOSE.

ON, TOOTH-GNASHER! ON, TOOTH-GRINDER! RACE THE LIGHTNING!

SO THOR AND BILL THUNDER PAST THE STARS, TRACKING THE DEMON WAVE THAT SEEMS TO FLOW ENDLESSLY PAST THEM...

...MOVING AT SUCH GREAT SPEED THAT THEY ARE INVISIBLE TO EVERY DEMONIC EYE...

...UNTIL AT LAST THEY REACH THE CORE OF THE GALAXY THAT ONCE HOUSED THE CIVILIZATION OF BILL'S PEOPLE.

BY THE BRISTLING BEARD OF ODIN!

MY HOME! MY HOME! WHAT HAVE THEY DONE TO YOU?

FOR BEFORE THEM LIE NOT THE RADIANT STARS OF AN ANCIENT AND WISE RACE...

...BUT A GLOWING PORTAL, PULSING WITH EVIL, OUT OF WHICH STREAMS A NUMBER-LESS HORDE OF DEMONS INTO THE UNIVERSE OF MEN!

WOE THAT THE VERY STARS WHICH GAVE ME LIFE SHOULD BE HARNESSED NOW TO CREATE SUCH EVIL!

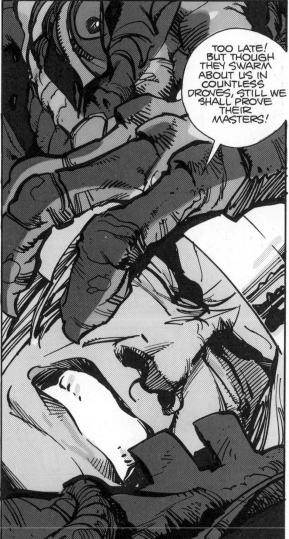

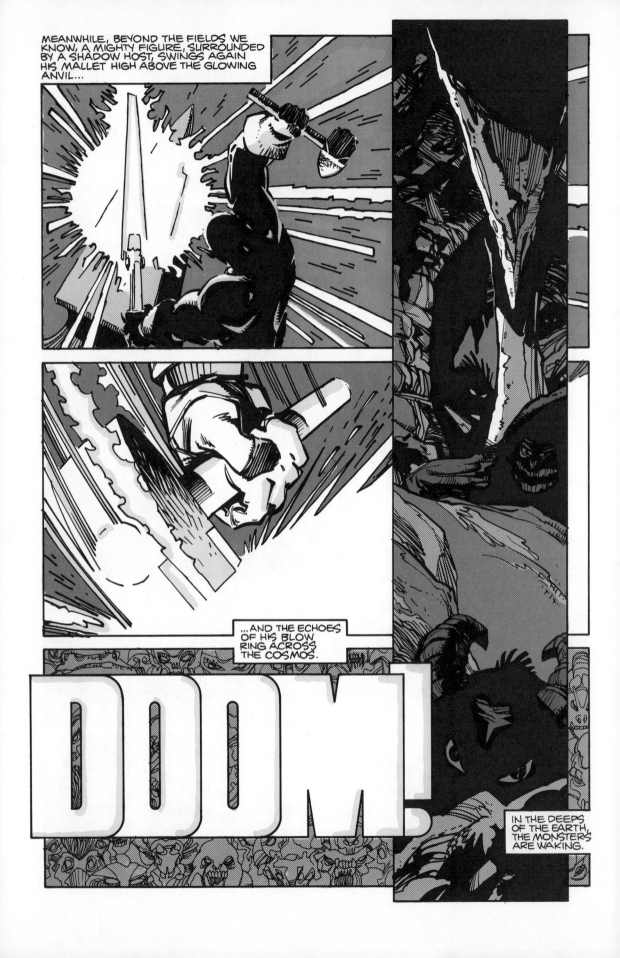

WHILE FAR AWAY, IN THE GREAT FLEET...

NO DEMON HAS YET GOTTEN PAST ME, BUT THEIR NUMBERS INCREASE WITH EVERY SECOND.

AND NOW THEY HAVE BEGUN TO MASS TO-GETHER FOR THEIR FINAL ATTACK!

VERY WELL! IF TODAY I MUST JOURNEY TO THE HALLS OF HELA, I SHALL NOT TRAVEL ALONE!

COME, DEMONS! WHO WILL BE THE FIRST TO TASTE THIS SWEET STEEL?

BADDOOM! BADDOOM!

WHA--!

THAT SHIP! IT MUST BE BILL'S **SKUTTLE-BUTT!**

INDEED I AM, MILADY. REPAIRED AND RETURNED TO DUTY. JUST IN TIME IT WOULD SEEM.

AND THOUGH I DO NOT RECOGNIZE YOU, YOU MUST BE A FRIEND OF MY MASTER TO FIGHT HIS BATTLES.

LEAP ABOARD AND WE SHALL FIGHT TOGETHER.

WELL SAID. I AM SIF, WARRIOR MAID OF ASGARD.

BILL AND HIS COMPANION—THOR—HAVE JOURNEYED OFF TO FIND THE SOURCE OF THESE DEMONS AND DESTROY IT.

IN THE MEANTIME, I REMAIN BEHIND TO GUARD THE FLEET AND ITS PRECIOUS CARGO.

THEN LET US BEGIN. THESE CREATURES SEEM SINGLE-MINDEDLY DETERMINED TO DESTROY US.

PERHAPS WE CAN LEAD THEM AWAY FROM THE FLEET AND GIVE BILL AND HIS COMPANION A CHANCE TO FINISH THEIR JOB!

BUT AS THE DEMONS TURN FROM THE FLEET IN HOT PURSUIT, LET US TURN TO THE GARDENS OF ASGARD TO LISTEN TO VALOROUS VOLSTAGG CONCLUDE HIS CHILLING TALE OF THE DEATH OF BALDER...

SO, MY YOUNG FRIEND, NOBLE BALDER WENT DOWN TO NIFFLEHEIM, HELA'S DARK DOMAIN.

HE FOUND THAT THE LEGENDS OF THE AFTER-LIFE WERE TRUE.

BEFORE HIM, DANK AND CHEERLESS, LAY THE CORPSE STRAND, THE HALLS OF THE TORTURED...

...AND THE DRAGON, NID-HOGG, THE EATER OF THE DEAD...

...CONSUMING THE SOULS OF THOSE WHO HAVE FLED IN TERROR DEEP INTO NIFFLEHEIM PAST THE GREAT WOLF GARM.

WHEN HE LOOKED UPON THE DEAD, HE WAS FILLED WITH HORROR...

...FOR THERE BEFORE HIM WERE THE VERY WARRIORS WHOM HE HIMSELF HAD SLAIN AND SENT TO NIFFLEHEIM IN BATTLES PAST!

THESE WERE THE FRUITS OF HIS MANY VICTORIES!

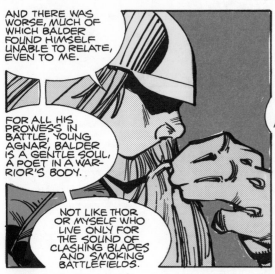

AND THERE WAS WORSE, MUCH OF WHICH BALDER FOUND HIMSELF UNABLE TO RELATE, EVEN TO ME.

FOR ALL HIS PROWESS IN BATTLE, YOUNG AGNAR, BALDER IS A GENTLE SOUL, A POET IN A WARRIOR'S BODY.

NOT LIKE THOR OR MYSELF WHO LIVE ONLY FOR THE SOUND OF CLASHING BLADES AND SMOKING BATTLEFIELDS.

OF COURSE I HAVE—UMMPH—GROWN SO—UGGH—LARGE THAT NO ORDINARY FOE IS WORTHY OF MY GREAT ABILITIES.

GROAN.

SURELY IF SOME HARM CAME NOW TO BALDER AND YOU WERE RESPONSIBLE, WHY I MIGHT EVEN FIND IT IN MY HEART, SO MUCH LARGER THAN THAT OF ORDINARY MEN, TO FORGIVE YOU.

LET ME DUST YOU OFF.

Paf Paf

OWOWOW.

WHY, EVEN THOR OR FANDRAL THE DASHING MIGHT FORGIVE YOU BE- CAUSE THEY WERE ONCE YOUNG AND DARING THEMSELVES.

POMPOUS OLD WINDBAG!

BUT HOGUN THE GRIM?

URK!

HOGUN WAS NEVER YOUNG. HE WOULD NEVER FORGET...

...OR FORGIVE!

MEANWHILE, IN THE DISTANT GALACTIC CORE...

IT IS NO GOOD, THOR! EVEN OUR COMBINED MIGHT IS UNABLE TO FORCE AN ENTRANCE THROUGH THE PORTAL!

THE POWER WITHIN IS TOO GREAT!

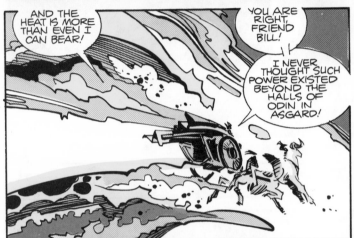

AND THE HEAT IS MORE THAN EVEN I CAN BEAR!

YOU ARE RIGHT, FRIEND BILL!

I NEVER THOUGHT SUCH POWER EXISTED BEYOND THE HALLS OF ODIN IN ASGARD!

YET THOUGH WE CANNOT ENTER, WE MAY STILL BE ABLE TO CLOSE THE PORTAL FOREVER TO THE DEMON HORDE AND SAVE YOUR PEOPLE!

STAND BESIDE THE PORTAL HERE AND AWAIT MY CALL.

I WILL TAKE MYSELF TO THE OTHER SIDE AND TOGETHER, WE MAY DO WHAT NEITHER OF US COULD ACCOMPLISH ALONE!

THEY'RE GONE!

BILL... AND THOR... MUST HAVE DESTROYED... THE DEMONS' SOURCE...

...WE'VE... WON...

SIF?

I'LL BE ALLRIGHT, SKUTTLEBUTT. I'M JUST... SO TIRED. BUT BILL... AND THOR?

STILL ALIVE, MY SENSORS TELL ME. AND RETURNING HERE.

BUT THERE IS MORE TO YOUR STORY THAN A SIMPLE FRIENDSHIP WITH BILL. THE OFFERING OF ONE'S LIFE FOR ANOTHER IS NO SMALL GIFT. AS I WELL KNOW.

LET US TALK AS WE RETURN TO THE FLEET TO WAIT. I, TOO, WOULD LEARN MORE ABOUT YOU ...AND BILL.

AT THAT MOMENT, IN A PENTHOUSE OVERLOOKING CENTRAL PARK IN NEW YORK CITY...

YOU NEEDN'T WORRY. I AM NOT UNSKILLED IN GETTING WHAT I WANT.

I DARE SAY. BUT HAVE A CARE, LORELEI.

THOR IS NO ORDINARY BUMPKIN TO SWOON AT YOUR FEET.

PERHAPS NOT. STILL, I HAVE MANY CHARMS WHICH I AM CERTAIN WILL ASSIST ME IN HIS DIRECTION.

BUT YOU, LOKI. YOU HAVE AIDED ME IN THIS ENDEAVOR.

IT WILL AMUSE ME, LADY.

IT WILL AMUSE ME GREATLY.

WHAT REWARD DO YOU LOOK TO RECEIVE OUT OF THIS GAME?

THE NIGHT DRAWS ITS VEIL ACROSS NEW YORK CITY, BUT IN THE MORNING LIGHT OF ASGARD, WE FIND THE STALWART WATCHMAN OF THE GODS...

STAND AND IDENTIFY YOUR-SELVES IF YOU SEEK TO CROSS THE RAINBOW BRIDGE INTO THE GOLDEN REALM!

GREETINGS, HEIM-DALL! WE HAVE RE-TURNED FROM THE FAR REACHES OF SPACE WITH A VICTORY!

THE LADY SIF, BETA RAY BILL, SKUTTLEBUTT, AND I BRING NEWS OF THE DE-STRUCTION OF OUR FOES!

WELL MET, MIGHTY THOR! LORD ODIN HAS PROCLAIMED YOUR TRIUMPH ACROSS THE LAND.

EVEN NOW, THE FEAST IS MADE READY. I GIVE YOU LEAVE TO ENTER.

WHILE SKUTTLEBUTT REMAINS OUTSIDE (FOR THERE ARE NO HALLS IN ASGARD LARGE ENOUGH TO HOLD HER)...

...THOR AND HIS COM-PANIONS ENTER THE CITY TO THE CHEERS OF THE THRONG!

STILL, EVEN HEROES NEED BATHS AND AS OUR COMRADES CHANGE INTO FRESH CLOTHING TO PREPARE FOR THE FEAST...

YOU ARE STRANGELY SILENT, FRIEND BILL. I HOPE YOU DO NOT FEEL THAT I HOLD A GRUDGE AGAINST YOU FOR YOUR VICTORY EARLIER AGAINST ME.*

AND AS FOR YOUR PEOPLE, WE DID WIN, YOU KNOW.

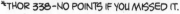

*THOR 338—NO POINTS IF YOU MISSED IT.

FEAR NOT, MY FRIEND. YOUR FRIENDSHIP IS BEYOND RE-PROACH. AS IS OUR VICTORY.

BUT I MUST SHORTLY RETURN TO GUIDE MY PEOPLE TO A NEW HOME AND THOUGH I CAN HARDLY BELIEVE IT, I AM LOATH TO LEAVE ASGARD...

...AND ALL THAT I HAVE FOUND HERE.

THE UNCOMPROMISING ACCEPTANCE I HAVE HAD WHEN EVEN MY OWN PEOPLE CAN SCARCELY LOOK AT ME, THE JOY OF COMRADESHIP, EVEN THE TOUCH OF A WOMAN'S HAND...

BUT I SAY TOO MUCH.

I AM WHAT I AM AND CANNOT CHANGE IT.

I SHALL SEE YOU AT DINNER.

ELSEWHERE...

YOU SENT FOR ME, MY LORD.

THANK YOU FOR COMING SO QUICKLY, SIF.

I WOULD LIKE A FEW WORDS WITH YOU...ABOUT BILL.

I KNOW MORE THAN YOU MIGHT THINK, LADY, ABOUT YOUR FEELINGS FOR HIM. I, TOO, FIND HIM A MATCH FOR MY OWN SON IN MORE WAYS THAN ONE.

BUT THERE IS IN BILL A CORE OF MELANCHOLY THAT EVEN I CANNOT FATHOM.

I THOUGHT PERHAPS A WOMAN'S HEART WOULD KNOW WHAT I DO NOT.

MY HEART WOULD KNOW NO MORE THAN YOU, LORD ODIN, WERE IT NOT FOR SKUTTLEBUTT. FOR BILL'S SHIP AND I HAVE HAD A LONG TALK AND SHARED MANY SECRETS.

SHE HAS BEEN WITH HIM ON THEIR ODYSSEY AND KNOWS HIM BETTER THAN ANYONE. SHE KNOWS WHAT HE DID **NOT** TELL US HIMSELF.

FOR THOUGH HIS STORY WAS TRUE, IT WAS IN-COMPLETE!

"WHEN HE WAS CHOSEN TO BE THE GUARDIAN OF HIS PEOPLE, HE NEGLECTED TO TELL US OF THE GREAT GAMES THAT WERE HELD TO PICK THE MIGHTIEST CHAMPION.

"HOW HE WON OVER THOUSANDS OF OTHERS IN GRUELING TESTS OF POWER AND ENDURANCE.

"HOW, FROM AMONG THE PHYSICALLY ACCEPTABLE CANDI-DATES, THE BEST WERE CHOSEN IN A SERIES OF PSYCHO-LOGICAL EXAMINA-TIONS...

"THAT LEFT MOST OF THEM DEAD OR INSANE!

"OR HOW THE CREATION OF BETA RAY BILL WAS ACCOMPLISHED WITH PAIN BEYOND IMAGINING...

"...UNTIL OF ALL THOSE COURAGEOUS WARRIORS, ONLY HE SURVIVED THE DREADFUL PROCESS."

AND THE CHANGE WAS IRREVERSIBLE. HE WILL ALWAYS BE WHAT HE HAS BECOME.

WORST OF ALL, HIS OWN PEOPLE COULD HARDLY BEAR THE SIGHT OF HIM ONCE HE HAD BEEN FINISHED. YET HE WOULD DO IT ALL AGAIN IF NECESSARY.

OH, ALL-FATHER, HOW DO MORTALS ENDURE IT?

BE AT PEACE, SIF. LET US SEE WHAT WE CAN DO.

THAT EVENING, AFTER THE FEASTING IS NEARLY THROUGH...

LET ALL NOW BE SILENT! LORD ODIN WOULD ADDRESS THE HEROES!

MY CHILDREN, WE STAND NOW TO HONOR THESE TWO WHO HAVE GONE TO THE ENDS OF THE UNIVERSE AND RETURNED VICTORIOUS.

WHAT CAN WE GIVE SUCH WARRIORS THAT THEY DO NOT ALREADY POSSESS?

VERY LITTLE, FOR THE TRUE WARRIOR CARRIES WITHIN HIMSELF ALL THAT IS NECESSARY.

YET MY HEART TELLS ME THAT WE MAY STAND HERE TOGETHER FOR THE LAST TIME AND SOME TOKEN, TO REMIND A DISTANT TRAVELER OF HIS FRIENDS, SEEMS APPROPRIATE.

STEP FORWARD AND RAISE YOUR HAMMERS THAT I MAY BESTOW UPON YOU EACH A GIFT THAT I HOPE WILL BE WORTHY OF YOU.

TO YOU, MY SON, AND TO YOU, BILL, LET EACH RECEIVE WHAT IS NEEDFUL.

SO SPEAKS ODIN!

KRACALACTAKA!

I... I FEEL NO DIFFERENT!

PERHAPS NOT. BUT I HAD AN OLD ENCHANTMENT THAT HAS OUTLIVED ITS ORIGINAL PURPOSE.

WITH MINOR ALTERATIONS, I THOUGHT YOU MIGHT FIND IT USEFUL.

STRIKE YOUR HAMMER, STORM BREAKER, UPON THE GROUND.

GO ON!

STRIKE IT!

BARROOM!

AND SUDDENLY, THERE IS A DEAD SILENCE WITHIN THE HALL...

UNTIL AT LAST...

I...I AM MYSELF AGAIN!

I AM MYSELF AGAIN!

AND STORM BREAKER HAS BECOME A...A CANE!

AS I SAID, AN ENCHANTMENT THAT HAD OUTLIVED ITS PURPOSE. NOW, WHENEVER YOU NEED TO, STRIKE THE CANE UPON THE GROUND AND BETA RAY THOR WILL LIVE AGAIN.

MY LORD...

MY LORD...

STAND UP, NOBLE WARRIOR. YOU HAVE EARNED THE RIGHT.

WHAT SAY YOU, BILL, TO A JOUST NOW, EH?

BUT WAIT, IF ODIN'S ENCHANTMENT NOW RESTS WITHIN STORM BREAKER, WHAT OF MJOLNIR?

WHAT OF DONALD BLAKE?

HEAR ME, HOSTS OF ASGARD!

PRAISE THESE HEROES! BILL, WHO HAS BECOME THE SECOND SON I NEVER HAD!

AND THOR, WHO IS NOW AND FOREVER, INDIVISIBLY, THE FIRST SON OF ODIN, THE GOD OF THUNDER AND HEIR TO THE THRONE OF ASGARD!

THE CHEERING LASTS A LONG, LONG TIME.

BUT THOUGH THE FEAST RENEWS ITSELF AND LASTS BEYOND THE COCK'S CROW, AT LENGTH THE THRONGS DISPERSE AND GOODBYES ARE SAID.

I MUST GO, THOR! AS A WARRIOR MAIDEN, I HAVE BECOME BLUNT AND DULLED. I HAVE EVEN BELIEVED THINGS THAT I AM SURE NOW WERE BUT BETRAYALS OF MY EYES.

ON BILL'S QUEST, I MAY REGAIN MY TEMPER AS I NEVER COULD ON MIDGARD.*

DO NOT FORGET ME.

LADY, SOONER COULD I FORGET MY OWN NAME.

*EARTH

STAND TOGETHER AND I WILL SEND YOU TO YOUR SHIP THAT WAITS BEYOND THE RAINBOW BRIDGE.

FARE THEE WELL!

MAY YOU AND YOURS BE GRANTED SAFE HAVEN, BILL.

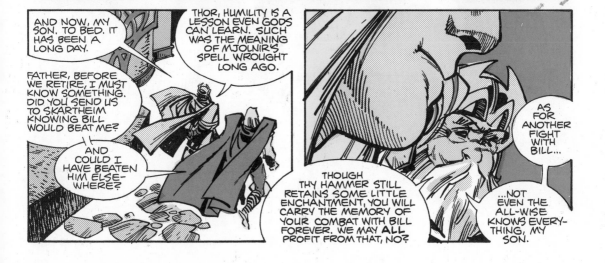

AND NOW, MY SON. TO BED. IT HAS BEEN A LONG DAY.

FATHER, BEFORE WE RETIRE, I MUST KNOW SOMETHING. DID YOU SEND US TO SKARTHEIM KNOWING BILL WOULD BEAT ME?

AND COULD I HAVE BEATEN HIM ELSEWHERE?

THOR, HUMILITY IS A LESSON EVEN GODS CAN LEARN. SUCH WAS THE MEANING OF MJOLNIR'S SPELL WROUGHT LONG AGO.

THOUGH THY HAMMER STILL RETAINS SOME LITTLE ENCHANTMENT, YOU WILL CARRY THE MEMORY OF YOUR COMBAT WITH BILL FOREVER. WE MAY ALL PROFIT FROM THAT, NO?

AS FOR ANOTHER FIGHT WITH BILL...

...NOT EVEN THE ALL-WISE KNOWS EVERYTHING, MY SON.